52 WEEK
SCRIPTURE REFLECTION

Prayer Journal
for women

BY LAUREN IBACH

This journal belongs to:

....

ABOUT THIS JOURNAL

Do you want to start a prayer journal, but the idea is a bit overwhelming? Perhaps you already keep a prayer journal, but your prayers feel stale and repetative. Regardless of where you're at in your experiences or perceptions of prayer journaling, this journal is for you.

I started a prayer journal when I first came to Christ. Writing has always been my most comfortable form of communication, so it was a very natural way for me to talk with God. However, as the years passed, I began to realize that my prayers were becoming very repetative and oftentimes, I would walk away from my quiet time feeling little to no added peace that should come from spending time with the Lord. This meant that I would oftentimes forgo prayer altogether, because it felt like a mundane ritual, which I knew was not God's design for prayer.

As I began growing and maturing in Christ, falling deeper in love with His Word and trusting more fully in His character and promises, my prayer life evolved as well. I learned how to pray the Word in a way that got me centered on who God is and what He says. This journal outlines that process. I still love freely praying to God based on what I'm feeling each day, but spending time praying through a Scripture passage—even if it's simply once per week—really helps shape my mindset as I approach God with my day-to-day requests.

God uses this way of praying to speak clearly to me through His Word, teach me more about Himself, and ground me in His promises, so that I keep coming back to Him ready for a new, refreshing time spent with Him.

I trust He will do the same for you.

In Christ,
Lauren Ibach

HOW TO USE THIS JOURNAL

This journal includes space for 52 entries so you can reflect and pray through one verse per week. I recommend committing to the same day and time each week to help you remain consistent. This is not meant to be your only prayer for the week, but is meant to help you center your thoughts on what God says in His Word as you continue in prayer each day.

You'll see that each journal entry leaves space for you to write a Bible verse, reflect on key truths from that passage, and pray through the truths that stood out to you. I'll give you some helpful tips below:

VERSE: Choose any verse or passage from the Bible you'd like. If you need help choosing one, there is a helpful list of verses at the end of this journal.

TRUTHS: Write down 1-3 truths that stand out to you in the verse. What do you learn about God? What do you learn about yourself and/or humanity? What's a promise you can cling to?

PRAISE: Prayers of praise focus on worshipping God for who He is. "You are" statements are great: "God, You are good, You are sovereign, You are Savior," or statements like, "Your love is steadfast." What can you praise God for that's communicated in the passage?

CONFESS: Confession is acknowledging and agreeing with God about our sins. What sins in your life does the verse highlight?

GIVE THANKS: This is where we thank God for what He has done for us. What does the passage prompt you to thank Him for?

ASK: What requests do you want to bring to the Lord after reflecting on your verse and praying through it? Are there any sins you need His help to overcome? Do you need help applying a specific truth to your current circumstances?

INDEX

VERSE(S)   PAGE #

_____   _____

_____   _____

_____   _____

_____   _____

_____   _____

_____   _____

_____   _____

_____   _____

_____   _____

_____   _____

_____   _____

_____   _____

_____   _____

_____   _____

_____   _____

_____   _____

_____   _____

_____   _____

_____   _____

_____   _____

_____   _____

_____   _____

_____   _____

VERSE(S)   **PAGE #**

Reflect on God's Word

VERSE: _____

_____

_____

_____

_____

_____

TRUTHS:

1. _____

2. _____

3. _____

Pray Through It

PRAISE: _____

_____

_____

_____

_____

CONFESS: _____

_____

_____

_____

_____

_____

GIVE THANKS: _____

_____

_____

_____

_____

ASK: _____

_____

_____

_____

_____

_____

_____

_____

_____

_____

_____

_____

_____

_____

_____

_____

_____

Reflect on God's Word

VERSE: _____

_____

_____

_____

_____

_____

TRUTHS:

1. _____

_____

2. _____

_____

3. _____

_____

Pray Through It

PRAISE: _____

_____

_____

_____

_____

_____

CONFESS: _____

_____

_____

_____

_____

_____

GIVE THANKS: _____

_____

_____

_____

_____

_____

ASK: _____

_____

_____

_____

_____

_____

_____

_____

_____

_____

_____

_____

_____

_____

_____

_____

Reflect on God's Word

VERSE: _____

_____

_____

_____

_____

_____

TRUTHS:

1. _____

_____

2. _____

_____

3. _____

_____

Pray Through It

PRAISE: _____

_____

_____

_____

_____

_____

CONFESS: _____

_____

_____

_____

_____

_____

GIVE THANKS: _____

_____

_____

_____

_____

ASK: _____

_____

_____

_____

_____

_____

_____

_____

_____

_____

_____

_____

_____

_____

Reflect on God's Word

VERSE: _____

_____

_____

_____

_____

_____

TRUTHS:

1. _____

_____

2. _____

_____

3. _____

_____

Pray Through It

PRAISE: _____

_____

_____

_____

_____

_____

CONFESS: _____

_____

_____

_____

_____

_____

GIVE THANKS: _____

_____

_____

_____

_____

_____

ASK: _____

_____

_____

_____

_____

_____

_____

_____

_____

_____

_____

_____

_____

_____

_____

_____

_____

_____

Reflect on God's Word

VERSE: _____

_____

_____

_____

_____

_____

TRUTHS:

1. _____

_____

2. _____

_____

3. _____

_____

Pray Through It

PRAISE: _____

_____

_____

_____

_____

_____

CONFESS: _____

_____

_____

_____

_____

_____

GIVE THANKS: _____

_____

_____

_____

_____

_____

ASK: _____

_____

_____

_____

_____

_____

_____

_____

_____

_____

_____

_____

_____

_____

_____

_____

_____

_____

God speaks
to us through
His Word

Reflect on God's Word

VERSE: _____

_____

_____

_____

_____

_____

TRUTHS:

1. _____

_____

2. _____

_____

3. _____

_____

Pray Through It

PRAISE: _____

_____

_____

_____

_____

_____

CONFESS: _____

_____

_____

_____

_____

_____

GIVE THANKS: _____

_____

_____

_____

_____

_____

ASK: _____

_____

_____

_____

_____

_____

_____

_____

_____

_____

_____

_____

_____

_____

_____

Reflect on God's Word

VERSE: _____

_____

_____

_____

_____

_____

TRUTHS:

1. _____

_____

2. _____

_____

3. _____

_____

Pray Through It

PRAISE: _____

_____

_____

_____

_____

_____

CONFESS: _____

_____

_____

_____

_____

_____

GIVE THANKS: _____

_____

_____

_____

_____

ASK: _____

_____

_____

_____

_____

_____

_____

_____

_____

_____

_____

_____

_____

_____

_____

_____

Reflect on God's Word

VERSE: _____

_____

_____

_____

_____

_____

TRUTHS:

1. _____

_____

2. _____

_____

3. _____

_____

Pray Through It

PRAISE: _____

_____

_____

_____

_____

_____

CONFESS: _____

_____

_____

_____

_____

_____

GIVE THANKS: _____

_____

_____

_____

_____

ASK: _____

_____

_____

_____

_____

_____

_____

_____

_____

_____

_____

_____

_____

_____

_____

_____

Reflect on God's Word

VERSE: _____

_____

_____

_____

_____

_____

TRUTHS:

1. _____

_____

2. _____

_____

3. _____

_____

Pray Through It

PRAISE: _____

_____

_____

_____

_____

_____

CONFESS: _____

_____

_____

_____

_____

_____

GIVE THANKS: _____

_____

_____

_____

_____

_____

ASK: _____

_____

_____

_____

_____

_____

_____

_____

_____

_____

_____

_____

_____

_____

_____

_____

_____

_____

Reflect on God's Word

VERSE: _____
_____
_____
_____
_____
_____

TRUTHS:

1. _____
_____

2. _____
_____

3. _____
_____

Pray Through It

PRAISE: _____
_____
_____
_____
_____
_____

CONFESS: _____
_____
_____
_____

_____

_____

GIVE THANKS: _____

_____

_____

_____

_____

ASK: _____

_____

_____

_____

_____

_____

_____

_____

_____

_____

_____

_____

_____

_____

_____

_____

Reflect on God's Word

VERSE: _____

_____

_____

_____

_____

_____

TRUTHS:

1. _____

_____

2. _____

_____

3. _____

_____

Pray Through It

PRAISE: _____

_____

_____

_____

_____

_____

CONFESS: _____

_____

_____

_____

GIVE THANKS: _____

ASK: _____

"Your word is a lamp
to my feet and a
light to my path."

Psalm 119:105

Reflect on God's Word

VERSE: _____
_____
_____
_____
_____
_____

TRUTHS:

1. _____
_____

2. _____
_____

3. _____
_____

Pray Through It

PRAISE: _____
_____
_____
_____
_____
_____

CONFESS: _____
_____
_____
_____

_____

_____

GIVE THANKS: _____

_____

_____

_____

_____

_____

ASK: _____

_____

_____

_____

_____

_____

_____

_____

_____

_____

_____

_____

_____

_____

_____

_____

_____

Reflect on God's Word

VERSE: _____
_____
_____
_____
_____
_____

TRUTHS:

1. _____
_____

2. _____
_____

3. _____
_____

Pray Through It

PRAISE: _____
_____
_____
_____
_____
_____

CONFESS: _____
_____
_____
_____

_____

_____

GIVE THANKS: _____

_____

_____

_____

_____

ASK: _____

_____

_____

_____

_____

_____

_____

_____

_____

_____

_____

_____

_____

_____

_____

Reflect on God's Word

VERSE: _____

_____

_____

_____

_____

_____

TRUTHS:

1. _____

_____

2. _____

_____

3. _____

_____

Pray Through It

PRAISE: _____

_____

_____

_____

_____

_____

CONFESS: _____

_____

_____

_____

_____

_____

GIVE THANKS: _____

_____

_____

_____

_____

_____

ASK: _____

_____

_____

_____

_____

_____

_____

_____

_____

_____

_____

_____

_____

_____

_____

_____

Reflect on God's Word

VERSE: _____

_____

_____

_____

_____

_____

TRUTHS:

1. _____

2. _____

3. _____

Pray Through It

PRAISE: _____

_____

_____

_____

_____

CONFESS: _____

_____

_____

_____

_____

_____

GIVE THANKS: _____

_____

_____

_____

_____

_____

ASK: _____

_____

_____

_____

_____

_____

_____

_____

_____

_____

_____

_____

_____

_____

_____

_____

Reflect on God's Word

VERSE: _____

_____

_____

_____

_____

_____

TRUTHS:

1. _____

_____

2. _____

_____

3. _____

_____

Pray Through It

PRAISE: _____

_____

_____

_____

_____

_____

CONFESS: _____

_____

_____

_____

_____

_____

GIVE THANKS: _____

_____

_____

_____

_____

ASK: _____

Reflect on God's Word

VERSE: _____

_____

_____

_____

_____

_____

TRUTHS:

1. _____

_____

2. _____

_____

3. _____

_____

Pray Through It

PRAISE: _____

_____

_____

_____

_____

_____

CONFESS: _____

_____

_____

_____

_____

_____

GIVE THANKS: _____

_____

_____

_____

_____

_____

ASK: _____

_____

_____

_____

_____

_____

_____

_____

_____

_____

_____

_____

_____

_____

_____

_____

_____

praying
God's Word is
conversational.

We are responding
to what God has
already spoken &
He is listening.

Reflect on God's Word

VERSE: _____

_____

_____

_____

_____

_____

TRUTHS:

1. _____

_____

2. _____

_____

3. _____

_____

Pray Through It

PRAISE: _____

_____

_____

_____

_____

_____

CONFESS: _____

_____

_____

_____

_____

_____

GIVE THANKS: _____

_____

_____

_____

_____

_____

ASK: _____

_____

_____

_____

_____

_____

_____

_____

_____

_____

_____

_____

_____

_____

_____

_____

_____

Reflect on God's Word

VERSE: _____
_____
_____
_____
_____
_____

TRUTHS:

1. _____
_____

2. _____
_____

3. _____
_____

Pray Through It

PRAISE: _____
_____
_____
_____
_____
_____

CONFESS: _____
_____
_____
_____

_____

_____

GIVE THANKS: _____

_____

_____

_____

_____

ASK: _____

_____

_____

_____

_____

_____

_____

_____

_____

_____

_____

_____

_____

_____

_____

Reflect on God's Word

VERSE: _____

_____

_____

_____

_____

_____

TRUTHS:

1. _____

2. _____

3. _____

Pray Through It

PRAISE: _____

_____

_____

_____

_____

_____

CONFESS: _____

_____

_____

_____

_____

_____

GIVE THANKS: _____

_____

_____

_____

_____

_____

ASK: _____

_____

_____

_____

_____

_____

_____

_____

_____

_____

_____

_____

_____

_____

_____

_____

_____

Reflect on God's Word

VERSE: _____
_____
_____
_____
_____
_____

TRUTHS:

1. _____
_____

2. _____
_____

3. _____
_____

Pray Through It

PRAISE: _____
_____
_____
_____
_____
_____

CONFESS: _____
_____
_____
_____

_____

_____

GIVE THANKS: _____

_____

_____

_____

_____

_____

ASK: _____

_____

_____

_____

_____

_____

_____

_____

_____

_____

_____

_____

_____

_____

_____

_____

Reflect on God's Word

VERSE: _____
_____
_____
_____
_____
_____

TRUTHS:
1. _____
_____
2. _____
_____
3. _____
_____

Pray Through It

PRAISE: _____
_____
_____
_____
_____
_____

CONFESS: _____
_____
_____
_____

GIVE THANKS: _____

_____

_____

_____

_____

ASK: _____

_____

_____

_____

_____

_____

_____

_____

_____

_____

_____

_____

_____

Reflect on God's Word

VERSE: _____
_____
_____
_____
_____
_____

TRUTHS:
1. _____
_____
2. _____
_____
3. _____
_____

Pray Through It

PRAISE: _____
_____
_____
_____
_____
_____

CONFESS: _____
_____
_____
_____

_____

_____

GIVE THANKS: _____

_____

_____

_____

_____

_____

ASK: _____

_____

_____

_____

_____

_____

_____

_____

_____

_____

_____

_____

_____

_____

_____

_____

_____

"All Scripture is breathed out by God and profitable for teaching, for reproof, for correction, and for training in righteousness,"

2 Timothy 3:16

Reflect on God's Word

VERSE: _____

_____

_____

_____

_____

TRUTHS:

1. _____

2. _____

3. _____

Pray Through It

PRAISE: _____

_____

_____

_____

_____

CONFESS: _____

_____

_____

_____

_____

GIVE THANKS: _____

_____

_____

_____

_____

ASK: _____

_____

_____

_____

_____

_____

_____

_____

_____

_____

_____

_____

_____

_____

_____

_____

_____

Reflect on God's Word

VERSE: _____
_____
_____
_____
_____
_____

TRUTHS:

1. _____
_____

2. _____
_____

3. _____
_____

Pray Through It

PRAISE: _____
_____
_____
_____
_____
_____

CONFESS: _____
_____
_____
_____

_____

_____

GIVE THANKS: _____

_____

_____

_____

_____

_____

ASK: _____

_____

_____

_____

_____

_____

_____

_____

_____

_____

_____

_____

_____

_____

_____

_____

_____

Reflect on God's Word

VERSE: _____

_____

_____

_____

_____

_____

TRUTHS:

1. _____

_____

2. _____

_____

3. _____

_____

Pray Through It

PRAISE: _____

_____

_____

_____

_____

_____

CONFESS: _____

_____

_____

_____

_____

_____

GIVE THANKS: _____

_____

_____

_____

_____

ASK: _____

_____

_____

_____

_____

_____

_____

_____

_____

_____

_____

_____

_____

_____

_____

Reflect on God's Word

VERSE: _____

_____

_____

_____

_____

_____

TRUTHS:

1. _____

_____

2. _____

_____

3. _____

_____

Pray Through It

PRAISE: _____

_____

_____

_____

_____

_____

CONFESS: _____

_____

_____

_____

_____

_____

GIVE THANKS: _____

_____

_____

_____

_____

ASK: _____

_____

_____

_____

_____

_____

_____

_____

_____

_____

_____

_____

_____

_____

_____

_____

Reflect on God's Word

VERSE: _____

_____

_____

_____

_____

_____

TRUTHS:

1. _____

_____

2. _____

_____

3. _____

_____

Pray Through It

PRAISE: _____

_____

_____

_____

_____

_____

CONFESS: _____

_____

_____

_____

_____

_____

GIVE THANKS: _____

_____

_____

_____

_____

_____

ASK: _____

_____

_____

_____

_____

_____

_____

_____

_____

_____

_____

_____

_____

_____

_____

_____

_____

Reflect on God's Word

VERSE: _____

_____

_____

_____

_____

_____

TRUTHS:

1. _____

_____

2. _____

_____

3. _____

_____

Pray Through It

PRAISE: _____

_____

_____

_____

_____

_____

CONFESS: _____

_____

_____

_____

_____

_____

GIVE THANKS: _____

_____

_____

_____

_____

ASK: _____

_____

_____

_____

_____

_____

_____

_____

_____

_____

_____

_____

_____

_____

_____

_____

_____

The Word
of God
is living
& active...

Hebrews
4:12

Reflect on God's Word

VERSE: _____

_____

_____

_____

_____

_____

TRUTHS:

1. _____

_____

2. _____

_____

3. _____

_____

Pray Through It

PRAISE: _____

_____

_____

_____

_____

_____

CONFESS: _____

_____

_____

_____

_____

_____

GIVE THANKS: _____

_____

_____

_____

_____

_____

ASK: _____

_____

_____

_____

_____

_____

_____

_____

_____

_____

_____

_____

_____

_____

_____

_____

_____

Reflect on God's Word

VERSE: _____
_____
_____
_____
_____
_____

TRUTHS:

1. _____
_____

2. _____
_____

3. _____
_____

Pray Through It

PRAISE: _____
_____
_____
_____
_____
_____

CONFESS: _____
_____
_____
_____

_____

_____

GIVE THANKS: _____

_____

_____

_____

_____

ASK: _____

_____

_____

_____

_____

_____

_____

_____

_____

_____

_____

_____

_____

_____

_____

Reflect on God's Word

VERSE: _____
_____
_____
_____
_____
_____

TRUTHS:

1. _____
_____

2. _____
_____

3. _____
_____

Pray Through It

PRAISE: _____
_____
_____
_____
_____
_____

CONFESS: _____
_____
_____
_____

_____

_____

GIVE THANKS: _____

_____

_____

_____

_____

ASK: _____

_____

_____

_____

_____

_____

_____

_____

_____

_____

_____

_____

_____

_____

_____

_____

_____

Reflect on God's Word

VERSE: _____

_____

_____

_____

_____

TRUTHS:

1. _____

2. _____

3. _____

Pray Through It

PRAISE: _____

_____

_____

_____

_____

CONFESS: _____

_____

_____

_____

_____

_____

GIVE THANKS: _____

_____

_____

_____

_____

ASK: _____

_____

_____

_____

_____

_____

_____

_____

_____

_____

_____

_____

_____

_____

_____

Reflect on God's Word

VERSE: _____

_____

_____

_____

_____

_____

TRUTHS:

1. _____

2. _____

3. _____

Pray Through It

PRAISE: _____

_____

_____

_____

_____

CONFESS: _____

_____

_____

_____

_____

_____

GIVE THANKS: _____

_____

_____

_____

_____

ASK: _____

_____

_____

_____

_____

_____

_____

_____

_____

_____

_____

_____

_____

_____

_____

_____

Reflect on God's Word

VERSE: _____

_____

_____

_____

_____

_____

TRUTHS:

1. _____

_____

2. _____

_____

3. _____

_____

Pray Through It

PRAISE: _____

_____

_____

_____

_____

_____

CONFESS: _____

_____

_____

_____

_____

_____

GIVE THANKS: _____

_____

_____

_____

_____

_____

ASK: _____

_____

_____

_____

_____

_____

_____

_____

_____

_____

_____

_____

_____

_____

_____

_____

_____

_____

pray more, worry less.

Reflect on God's Word

VERSE: _____

_____

_____

_____

_____

_____

TRUTHS:

1. _____

2. _____

3. _____

Pray Through It

PRAISE: _____

_____

_____

_____

_____

CONFESS: _____

_____

_____

_____

_____

_____

GIVE THANKS: _____

_____

_____

_____

_____

ASK: _____

_____

_____

_____

_____

_____

_____

_____

_____

_____

_____

_____

_____

_____

_____

Reflect on God's Word

VERSE: _____

_____

_____

_____

_____

_____

TRUTHS:

1. _____

2. _____

3. _____

Pray Through It

PRAISE: _____

_____

_____

_____

_____

_____

CONFESS: _____

_____

_____

_____

_____

_____

GIVE THANKS: _____

_____

_____

_____

_____

_____

ASK: _____

_____

_____

_____

_____

_____

_____

_____

_____

_____

_____

_____

_____

_____

_____

_____

_____

Reflect on God's Word

VERSE: _____

_____

_____

_____

_____

_____

TRUTHS:

1. _____

_____

2. _____

_____

3. _____

_____

Pray Through It

PRAISE: _____

_____

_____

_____

_____

_____

CONFESS: _____

_____

_____

_____

_____

_____

GIVE THANKS: _____

_____

_____

_____

_____

ASK: _____

_____

_____

_____

_____

_____

_____

_____

_____

_____

_____

_____

_____

_____

_____

Reflect on God's Word

VERSE: _____

_____

_____

_____

_____

_____

TRUTHS:

1. _____

2. _____

3. _____

Pray Through It

PRAISE: _____

_____

_____

_____

_____

_____

CONFESS: _____

_____

_____

_____

GIVE THANKS: _____

ASK: _____

Reflect on God's Word

VERSE: _____

_____

_____

_____

_____

_____

TRUTHS:

1. _____

2. _____

3. _____

Pray Through It

PRAISE: _____

_____

_____

_____

_____

CONFESS: _____

_____

_____

_____

_____

_____

GIVE THANKS: _____

_____

_____

_____

_____

ASK: _____

_____

_____

_____

_____

_____

_____

_____

_____

_____

_____

_____

_____

_____

_____

_____

Reflect on God's Word

VERSE: _____

_____

_____

_____

_____

_____

TRUTHS:

1. _____

2. _____

3. _____

Pray Through It

PRAISE: _____

_____

_____

_____

_____

CONFESS: _____

_____

_____

_____

_____

_____

GIVE THANKS: _____

_____

_____

_____

_____

ASK: _____

_____

_____

_____

_____

_____

_____

_____

_____

_____

_____

_____

_____

_____

_____

"so shall my word be that goes out from my mouth; it shall not return to me empty, but it shall accomplish that which I purpose, and shall succeed in the thing for which I sent it."

Isaiah 55:11

Reflect on God's Word

VERSE: _____

_____

_____

_____

_____

_____

TRUTHS:

1. _____

2. _____

3. _____

Pray Through It

PRAISE: _____

_____

_____

_____

_____

CONFESS: _____

_____

_____

_____

_____

_____

GIVE THANKS: _____

_____

_____

_____

_____

_____

ASK: _____

_____

_____

_____

_____

_____

_____

_____

_____

_____

_____

_____

_____

_____

_____

Reflect on God's Word

VERSE: _____

_____

_____

_____

_____

_____

TRUTHS:

1. _____

_____

2. _____

_____

3. _____

_____

Pray Through It

PRAISE: _____

_____

_____

_____

_____

_____

CONFESS: _____

_____

_____

_____

_____

_____

GIVE THANKS: _____

_____

_____

_____

_____

ASK: _____

_____

_____

_____

_____

_____

_____

_____

_____

_____

_____

_____

_____

_____

_____

_____

Reflect on God's Word

VERSE: _____

_____

_____

_____

_____

TRUTHS:

1. _____

2. _____

3. _____

Pray Through It

PRAISE: _____

_____

_____

_____

_____

CONFESS: _____

_____

_____

_____

_____

_____

GIVE THANKS: _____

_____

_____

_____

_____

ASK: _____

_____

_____

_____

_____

_____

_____

_____

_____

_____

_____

_____

_____

_____

_____

Reflect on God's Word

VERSE: _____

_____

_____

_____

_____

_____

TRUTHS:

1. _____

2. _____

3. _____

Pray Through It

PRAISE: _____

_____

_____

_____

_____

_____

CONFESS: _____

_____

_____

_____

_____

_____

GIVE THANKS: _____

_____

_____

_____

_____

ASK: _____

_____

_____

_____

_____

_____

_____

_____

_____

_____

_____

_____

_____

_____

_____

_____

Reflect on God's Word

VERSE: _____
_____
_____
_____
_____
_____

TRUTHS:

1. _____
_____

2. _____
_____

3. _____
_____

Pray Through It

PRAISE: _____
_____
_____
_____
_____
_____

CONFESS: _____
_____
_____
_____

_____

_____

GIVE THANKS: _____

_____

_____

_____

_____

ASK: _____

_____

_____

_____

_____

_____

_____

_____

_____

_____

_____

_____

_____

_____

_____

_____

Reflect on God's Word

VERSE: _____
_____
_____
_____
_____
_____

TRUTHS:

1. _____
_____

2. _____
_____

3. _____
_____

Pray Through It

PRAISE: _____
_____
_____
_____
_____
_____

CONFESS: _____
_____
_____
_____

_____

_____

GIVE THANKS: _____

_____

_____

_____

_____

_____

ASK: _____

_____

_____

_____

_____

_____

_____

_____

_____

_____

_____

_____

_____

_____

_____

_____

_____

the Word
of the LORD
proves true

psalm 18:30

Reflect on God's Word

VERSE: _____

_____

_____

_____

_____

_____

TRUTHS:

1. _____

_____

2. _____

_____

3. _____

_____

Pray Through It

PRAISE: _____

_____

_____

_____

_____

_____

CONFESS: _____

_____

_____

_____

_____

_____

GIVE THANKS: _____

_____

_____

_____

_____

ASK: _____

_____

_____

_____

_____

_____

_____

_____

_____

_____

_____

_____

_____

_____

_____

_____

_____

Reflect on God's Word

VERSE: _____

_____

_____

_____

_____

_____

TRUTHS:

1. _____

2. _____

3. _____

Pray Through It

PRAISE: _____

_____

_____

_____

_____

CONFESS: _____

_____

_____

_____

_____

_____

GIVE THANKS: _____

_____

_____

_____

_____

ASK: _____

_____

_____

_____

_____

_____

_____

_____

_____

_____

_____

_____

_____

_____

_____

_____

Reflect on God's Word

VERSE: _____

_____

_____

_____

_____

_____

TRUTHS:

1. _____

_____

2. _____

_____

3. _____

_____

Pray Through It

PRAISE: _____

_____

_____

_____

_____

CONFESS: _____

_____

_____

_____

_____

_____

GIVE THANKS: _____

_____

_____

_____

_____

_____

ASK: _____

_____

_____

_____

_____

_____

_____

_____

_____

_____

_____

_____

_____

_____

_____

_____

Reflect on God's Word

VERSE: _____
_____
_____
_____
_____
_____

TRUTHS:

1. _____
_____

2. _____
_____

3. _____
_____

Pray Through It

PRAISE: _____
_____
_____
_____
_____

CONFESS: _____
_____
_____
_____

_____

_____

GIVE THANKS: _____

_____

_____

_____

_____

_____

ASK: _____

_____

_____

_____

_____

_____

_____

_____

_____

_____

_____

_____

_____

_____

_____

_____

_____

Reflect on God's Word

VERSE: _____
_____
_____
_____
_____
_____

TRUTHS:

1. _____
_____

2. _____
_____

3. _____
_____

Pray Through It

PRAISE: _____
_____
_____
_____
_____
_____

CONFESS: _____
_____
_____
_____

_____

_____

GIVE THANKS: _____

_____

_____

_____

_____

_____

ASK: _____

_____

_____

_____

_____

_____

_____

_____

_____

_____

_____

_____

_____

_____

_____

_____

VERSE SUGGESTIONS...

ABOUT WHO GOD IS

Deuteronomy 7:9

Psalm 18:2

John 14:6

Romans 8:31

Hebrews 10:23

Revelation 4:11

ABOUT THE GOSPEL & GOD'S WORD

Psalm 119:105

John 3:16

Ephesians 2:4-5

Ephesians 2:8-9

2 Timothy 3:16

1 Peter 1:3

ABOUT WHO GOD SAYS WE ARE

Genesis 1:27

Psalm 139:13-14

John 15:16

Galatians 2:20

Ephesians 1:7

1 Peter 2:9

ABOUT LIVING OUT YOUR FAITH

Deuteronomy 13:4

Proverbs 3:5-6

Matthew 22:37-39

1 Corinthians 10:31

Galatians 5:22-23

Ephesians 4:29

Philippians 2:3-4

Philippians 4:8

FOR TIMES OF FEAR & ANXIETY

Joshua 1:9

Psalm 34:4

Proverbs 3:25-26

Isaiah 26:3

Isaiah 41:10

Matthew 6:34

Philippians 4:6-7

2 Timothy 1:7

FOR TIMES OF SUFFERING & HARDSHIP

Psalm 147:3	Isaiah 43:2
John 16:33	Romans 8:28
Romans 12:12	2 Corinthians 4:17
2 Corinthians 12:10	Philippians 4:19
James 1:2-3	1 Peter 4:12-13

FOR TIMES OF CONFUSION

Psalm 18:30	Psalm 32:8
Psalm 130:5	Isaiah 55:8
Jeremiah 33:3	John 14:27
1 Corinthians 14:33	Colossians 1:17

FOR TIMES OF GRATITUDE & REJOICING

1 Chronicles 16:34	Lamentations 3:22-23
1 Thessalonians 5:18	James 1:17

FOR WHEN YOU ARE WRESTLING WITH SIN

Psalm 32:5	Psalm 34:19
Acts 3:19-20	Romans 3:23-24
Hebrews 4:16	2 Peter:3:23-24

Made in the USA
Las Vegas, NV
27 November 2022